This book belongs to

....

THE ZIGZAG ZEBRA

a rhyming alphabet

Copyright © 2011 by All About Learning Press
Printed in the United States of America

All About Learning Press
2038 E. Anvil Lake Road
Eagle River, WI 54521

ISBN 978-1-935197-14-0

Editing and Page Layout: Renée M. LaTulippe
Cover Design: David LaTulippe
Illustrations: Donna Goeddaeus

The Zigzag Zebra: a rhyming alphabet is part of the All About Reading program. For more books in this series, go to www.AllAboutReading.com.

To the reader –

May you fly through these pages
like a clever bee,
learning letters and sounds
from A to Z

The alligator makes all critters afraid.

His teeth bite hard, and he crushes!

Alas! Do you think he brushes?

When bears eat blackberries,
they all should wear bibs.

Bees should wear bibs with their honey.

But boy, they sure would look funny!

Calico cats crunch cookies and candy.

They also sneak cereal with cream.

Getting caught is like a bad dream!

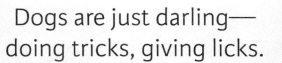

Dogs are just darling—
doing tricks, giving licks.

Some will even wear dresses.

It's a doozy
when they make big messes!

An elephant's ears are enormous,
and flap.

His eyes can get big like two eggs.

And when he smells peanuts, he begs!

Fat frogs can't fly, but they love to float.

They flip with all of their might.

It gives little fishes a fright!

Goodness! It's grinning guppies galore!

There's a gentle friend in each guppy.

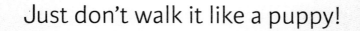

Just don't walk it like a puppy!

A hippo's so huge she can't even hide.

Her hips hog all of the path.

Help! Now she's taking a bath!

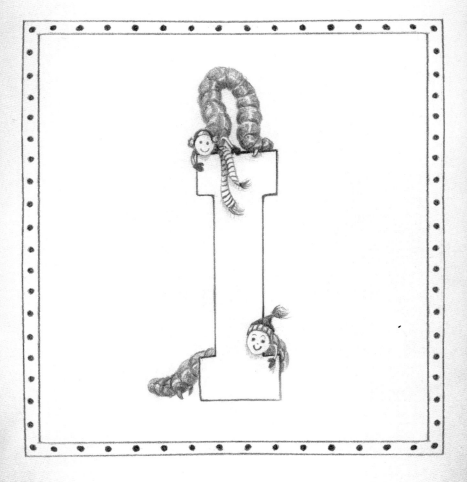

Imagine an inchworm sliding on ice.

The idea for two is quite chummy...

...two friends ski on one tummy!

The jolly jackrabbits jumped too fast.

Their legs got all in a jumble.

Jeepers! They just took a tumble!

A kangaroo kid is kissed and tucked in.

Mom keeps him close in her pocket.

Whee! She kicks off like a rocket!

Lily the Llama has lovely large eyes.

With smiles and long hair, she's a hit...

...but let her get mad, and she'll spit!

Mice might scare your mom
and grandma.

But there's much to admire
about a mouse...

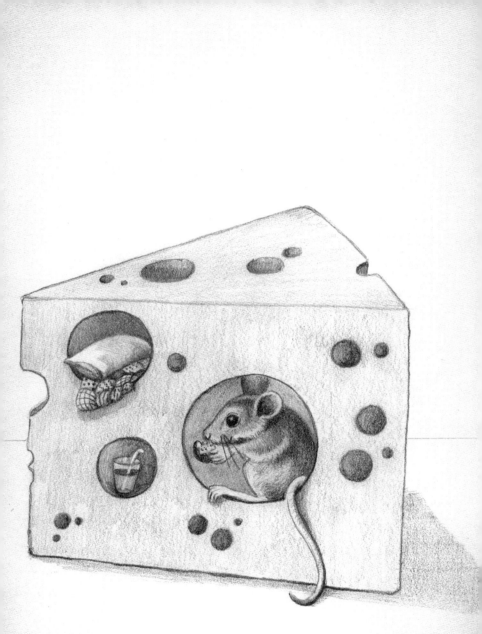

...like when his meal is also his house!

The neighbor's new goat
is a nightmare named Nelly.

She's naughty and nippy, this nanny.

Take note, or she'll butt your fanny!

An octopus hides on the ocean floor.

He often shoots ink, and he's smart.

Do you think he'd have fun learning art?

Two porcupine friends met on a path.

One kissed the other one's mug.

Then they shared a picky pin hug.

"Quack, quack," quipped the bird.
"Why do I quack?"

"A hen doesn't say 'quack,'
but says 'cluck'…"

"Oh! Maybe it's 'cause I'm a duck!"

A raccoon at a picnic is hard to resist.

He's a ridiculously fun little guy.

Till the rascal runs away with your pie!

It's safe to say "Yikes!"
when you see the white stripes.

A skunk! Take a quick detour...

...or you'll get all stinky for sure!

Tiny the Fly tried to tickle the toad.

He twittered and teased him a bunch.

Too bad...Tiny was lunch!

How could a penguin use an umbrella

when he comes up from the sea?

Oh, upside down, I see!

Violet was a very small snail.

She longed to vamoose and vroom...

...but an inch was all she could zoom!

He waddled, he wallowed,
he did a wet wobble.

The walrus was as big as can be.

No weensy wee lightweight was he!

The curious fox loves to explore.

It's fun, except when it's not!

And he gets in trouble a lot!

Gypsy, my yak, has a coat
that's all shaggy.

If she knit it like yarn, it'd be better.

Then she'd enjoy a nice sweater!

What if a zebra wasn't all stripes?

What if some zigzags
were zeroes instead?

He'd have a polka-dot head!

The End